What's My Style?

I love creating elaborate patterns packed with detail so I can do lots of intricate coloring. I try to use as many colors as possible. Then, I layer on lots of fun details. Here are some more examples of my work.

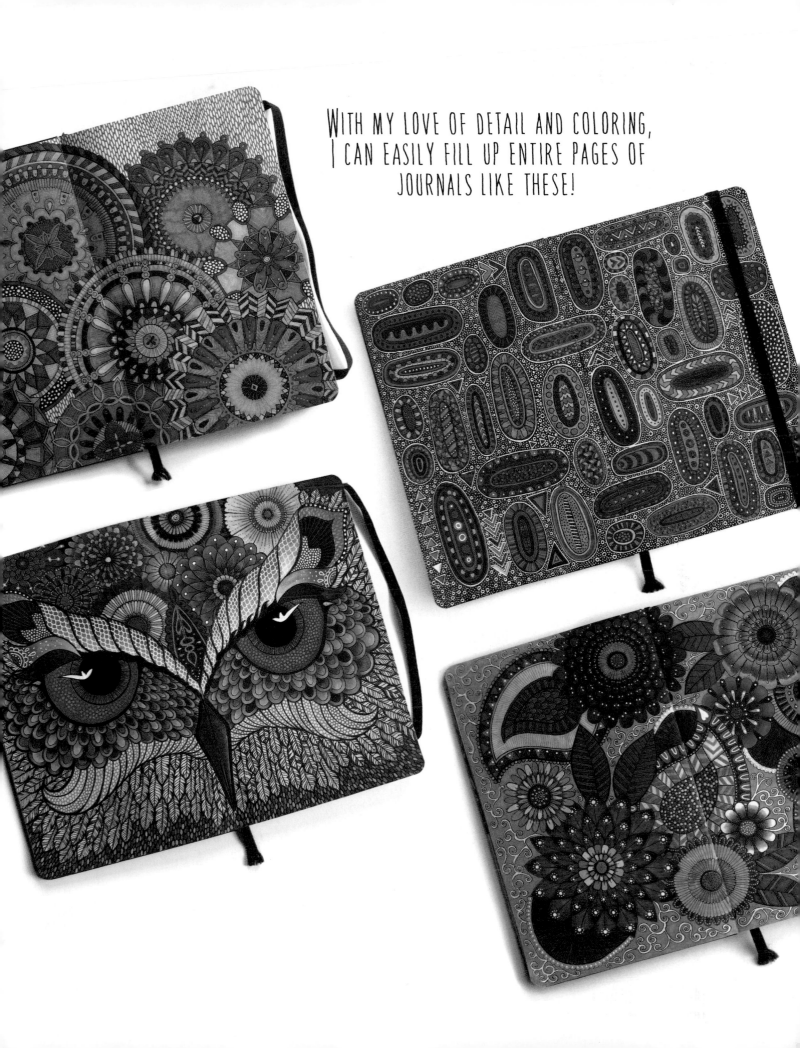

With my love of detail and coloring, I can easily fill up entire pages of journals like these!

Tips and Techniques

WHERE TO START

You might find putting color on a fresh page stressful. It's ok! Here are a few tricks I use to get the ink flowing.

Do you like warm colors?

How about cool colors?

Maybe you like warm and cool colors together!

Start with an easy decision. If a design has leaves, without a doubt, that's where I start. No matter how wacky and colorful everything else gets, I always color the leaves in my illustrations green. I have no reason for it, it's just how it is! Try to find something in the design to help ground you by making an easy color decision: leaves are green, the sky is blue, etc.

Get inspired. Take a good look at everything in the illustration. You chose to color it for a reason. One little piece that you love will jump out and say, "Color me! Use red, please!" Or maybe it will say blue, or pink, or green. Just relax—it will let you know.

Follow your instincts. What colors do you love? Are you a big fan of purple? Or maybe yellow is your favorite. If you love it, use it!

Just go for it. Close your eyes, pick up a color, point to a spot on the illustration, and start! Sometimes starting is the hardest part, but it's the fastest way to finish!

HELPFUL HINTS

There is no right or wrong. All colors work together, so don't be scared to mix it up. The results can be surprising!

Try it. Test your chosen colors on scrap paper before you start coloring your design. You can also test blending techniques and how to use different shapes and patterns for detail work—you can see how different media will blend with or show up on top of your chosen colors. I even use the paper to clean my markers or pens if necessary.

Make a color chart. A color chart is like a test paper for every single color you have! It provides a more accurate way to choose colors than selecting them based on the color of the marker's cap. To make a color chart, color a swatch with each marker, colored pencil, gel pen, etc. Label each swatch with the name or number of the marker so you can easily find it later.

Keep going. Even if you think you've ruined a piece, work through it. I go through the same cycle with my coloring: I love a piece at the beginning, and by the halfway point I nearly always dislike it. Sometimes by the end I love it again, and sometimes I don't, and that's ok. It's important to remember that you're coloring for you—no one else. If you really don't like a piece at the end, stash it away and remember that you learned something. You know what not to do next time. My studio drawers are full of everything from duds to masterpieces!

Be patient. Let markers, gel pens, and paints dry thoroughly between each layer. There's nothing worse than smudging a cluster of freshly inked dots across the page with your hand. Just give them a minute to dry and you can move on to the next layer.

Use caution. Juicy/inky markers can "spit" when you uncap them. Open them away from your art piece.

Work from light to dark. It's much easier to make something darker gradually than to lighten it.

Shade with gray. A mid—tone lavender—gray marker is perfect for adding shadows to your artwork, giving it depth and making it pop right off the page!

Try blending fluid. If you like working with alcohol—based markers, a refillable bottle of blending fluid or a blending pen is a great investment. Aside from enabling you to easily blend colors together, it can help clean up unwanted splatters or mistakes—it may not take some colors away completely, but it will certainly lighten them. I use it to clean the body of my markers as I'm constantly smudging them with inky fingers. When a marker is running out of ink, I find adding a few drops of blending fluid to the ink barrel will make it last a bit longer.

LAYERING AND BLENDING

I love layering and blending colors. It's a great way to create shading and give your finished piece lots of depth and dimension. The trick is to work from the lightest color to the darkest and then go over everything again with the lightest shade to keep the color smooth and bring all the layers together.

1 Apply a base layer with the lightest color.

2 Add the middle color, using it to create shading.

3 Smooth out the color by going over everything with the lightest color.

4 Add the darkest color, giving your shading even more depth. Use the middle color to go over the same area you colored in Step 2.

5 Go over everything with the lightest color as you did in Step 3.

PATTERNING AND DETAILS

Layering and blending will give your coloring depth and dimension. Adding patterning and details will really bring it to life. If you're not convinced, try adding a few details to one of your colored pieces with a white gel pen—that baby will make magic happen! Have fun adding all of the dots, doodles, and swirls you can imagine.

1 Once you've finished your coloring, blending, and layering, go back and add simple patterning like lines or dots. You can add your patterns in black or color. For this leaf, I used two different shades of green pen.

2 Now it's time to add some fun details using paint pens or gel pens. Here, I used white, yellow, and more green.

This design really pops with lots of patterning and little details.

Coloring Supplies

I'm always asked about the mediums I use to color my illustrations. The answer would be really long if I listed every single thing, so here are a few of my favorites. Keep in mind, these are *my* favorites. When you color, you should use YOUR favorites!

Alcohol-based markers. I have many, and a variety of brands. My favorites have a brush nib—it's so versatile. A brush nib is perfect for tiny, tight corners, but also able to cover a large, open space easily. I find I rarely get streaking, and if I do, it's usually because the ink is running low!

Fine-tip pens. Just like with markers, I have lots of different pens. I use them for my layers of detail work and for the itsy bitsy spots my markers can't get into.

Paint pens. These are wonderful! Because the ink is usually opaque, they stand out really well against a dark base color. I use extra fine point pens for their precision. Some paint pens are water based, so I can use a brush to blend the colors and create a cool watercolor effect.

Gel pens. I have a few, but I usually stick to white and neon colors that will stand out on top of dark base colors or other mediums.

Hello Angel #1017, Color by Hello Angel

Hello Angel #1026, Color by Hello Angel

Hello Angel #1032, Color by Erica Avedikian

Hello Angel #1007, Color by Erica Avedikian

Hello Angel #1001, Color by Hello Angel

Hello Angel #1029, Color by Dawn Collins

Hello Angel #1030, Color by Elaine Sampson

Hello Angel #1003, Color by Darla Tjelmeland

Hello Angel #1004, Color by Darla Tjelmeland

Sometimes your only available
transportation is a leap of faith.

—MARGARET SHEPARD

_____
_____
_____
_____
_____
_____
_____
_____
_____

The future is always beginning now.

—Mark Strand

If you surrender completely to the
moments as they pass,
you live more richly those moments.

—ANNE MORROW LINDBERGH

_____
_____
_____
_____
_____
_____
_____
_____
_____

If you want to conquer the anxiety of life,
live in the moment,
live in the breath.

—AMIT RAY

Whatever the present moment contains,
accept it as if you had chosen it.
Always work with it, not against it.

—ECKHART TOLLE

_____
_____
_____
_____
_____
_____
_____
_____
_____

An obstacle is often a stepping stone.

—Unknown

_____

_____

_____

_____

_____

_____

_____

_____

_____

The present moment is filled with joy
and happiness. If you are attentive,
you will see it.

—THICH NHAT HANH

_____
_____
_____
_____
_____
_____
_____
_____
_____
_____

Surrender to what is. Let go of what was.
Have faith in what will be.

—SONIA RICOTTI

If you want to know where your heart is,
look to where your mind goes
when it wanders.

—Unknown

In the end, just three things matter:
How well we have lived.
How well we have loved.
How well we have learned to let go.

—JACK KORNFIELD

Happiness doesn't have to be chased...
it merely has to be chosen.

—MANDY HALE

_____
_____
_____
_____
_____
_____
_____
_____

The basic root of happiness lies in our minds;
outer circumstances are nothing
more than adverse or favorable.

—Matthieu Ricard

The most precious gift we can offer
others is our presence.
When mindfulness embraces those we love,
they will bloom like flowers.

—THICH NHAT HANH

We are awakened to the profound
realization that the true path to liberation
is to let go of everything.

—JACK KORNFIELD

Happiness is your nature.
It is not wrong to desire it.
What is wrong is seeking it outside
when it is inside.

—Ramana Maharshi

In mindfulness one is not only
restful and happy, but alert and awake.
Meditation is not evasion;
it is a serene encounter with reality.

—THICH NHAT HANH

Those who are without compassion
cannot see what is seen with
the eyes of compassion.

—THICH NHAT HANH

Be happy in the moment, that's enough.
Each moment is all we need, not more.

—MOTHER TERESA

Don't believe everything you think.
Thoughts are just that—thoughts.

—ALLAN LOKOS

_____
_____
_____
_____
_____
_____
_____
_____
_____

Go as far as you can see; when you get there,
you'll be able to see farther.

—UNKNOWN

Mindfulness is the miracle which
can call back in a flash our dispersed
mind and restore it to wholeness so
that we can live each minute of life.

—UNKNOWN

> Respond; don't react.
> Listen; don't talk. Think; don't assume.
>
> —Raji Lukkoor

How wonderful it is that nobody
need wait a single moment
before starting to improve the world.

—ANNE FRANK

The grass is greener where you water it.

—UNKNOWN

Breathe and let be.

—Jon Kabat-Zinn

Everything you've ever wanted
is on the other side of fear.

—Unknown

_____
_____
_____
_____
_____
_____
_____
_____
_____

The place to be happy is here.
The time to be happy is now.

—ROBERT G. INGERSOLL

_____

Whether you think you can or think you can't—you are right.

—HENRY FORD

_____
_____
_____
_____
_____
_____
_____
_____
_____

May my heart be brave,
my mind fierce,
and my spirit free.

—UNKNOWN

Being happy doesn't mean that
everything is perfect.
It means that you've decided
to look beyond the imperfections.

—Unknown